Devon at Work:

Past and Present

Uniform with this book

Industrial History in Pictures: Scotland
Industrial History in Pictures: Bristol
The Lake District at Work: Past and Present

Devon at Work:
Past and Present

Walter Minchinton

David & Charles : Newton Abbot

0 7153 6389 1

Printed in Great Britain
by Edwin Snell . Yeovil Somerset
for David & Charles (Holdings) Limited
South Devon House Newton Abbot Devon

Contents

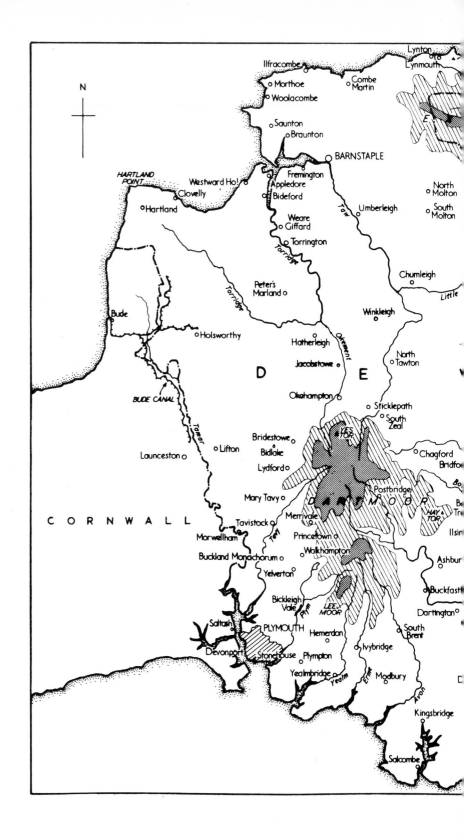

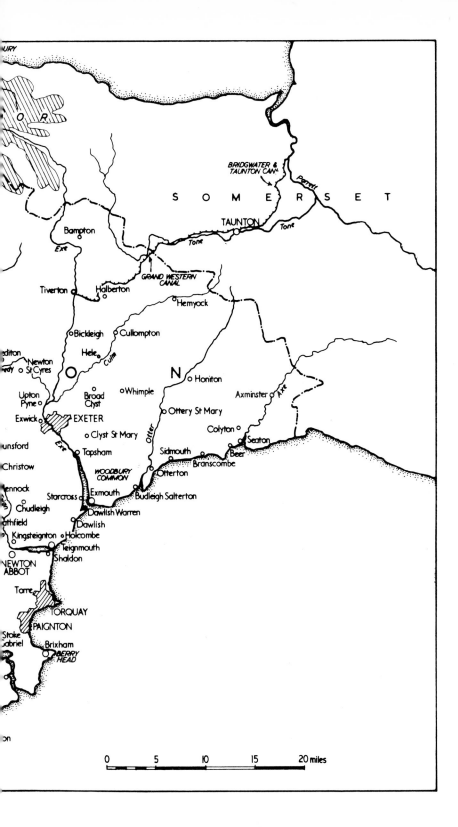

Introduction

For those who think of Devon in terms of cream teas and golden sands, red cliffs and thatched cottages, a volume devoted to Devon in a series on industrial history may seem incongruous. But a little reflection—and perhaps a perusal of the following pages—may go far to provide a justification for producing such a book which grew out of an industrial archaeology survey of Devon.

Several considerations have guided the selection of pictures. First of all as wide a range as possible of industrial activity has been covered though, as with companion volumes, agriculture and rural crafts have by and large been excluded. Where a choice was possible some attempt has been made to represent every part of the county. Then as wide a time range as possible and as great a variety of types of illustrations as could be discovered have been used. A reasonable balance between architectural features, machinery and people has been sought. But the search for variety has not been pushed to the point of eccentricity. All the major physical signs of industrial activity in the county are represented though sometimes with unfamiliar illustrations.

One purpose of this volume is to stimulate interest in the preservation of pictures of industrial activity by showing what a valuable record they provide of means of production which very quickly alter and are forgotten in an age of rapid technological change.

The subject has been interpreted widely to include associated aspects of economic activity. Illustrations of industrial processes inevitably give some indication of the social conditions of the workers concerned and the section on housing illustrates the living conditions of some of them. Industrial activity requires an outlet for its products and therefore sections on the ports which were essential to the trade and wealth of Devon and on the means of inland communication for the distribution of goods and the movement of workers have been included.

Exeter, April 1973   Walter Minchinton

Wool, Lace and Carpets

From the fourteenth century until the early nineteenth century Devon was one of the main English cloth-making counties. Spinning and weaving were very largely carried on in the home and the cloth was finished in the towns, such as Tavistock, Tiverton and Exeter, while water-driven fulling mills were to be found on many of the streams. The Devon cloths were kerseys and later serges which were small, light, brightly coloured and relatively cheap. The industry flourished in the seventeenth and eighteenth centuries but declined from the early nineteenth century. By the end of the last century, clothmaking was almost dead and now only a few mills, largely catering for the tourist trade, are working at Buckfastleigh, Dartington, Tavistock and Totnes.

This part of the Exeter section of Benjamin Donn's map of Devon, 1765, give some indication of the involvement of the city in woollen cloth manufacture in the eighteenth century. It shows Tuckers Hall, the fulling mills to the left of the quay (marked 13) and the open ground around the city where the cloth was stretched and bleached in the sun after it had been fulled

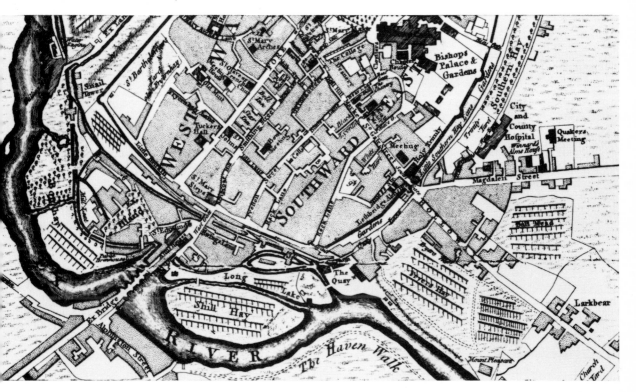

The Company of Weavers, Fullers and Shearmen of the city of Exeter, a company which once controlled cloth-making in the city, still survives. During Exeter's industrial and commercial heyday in the reign of Queen Anne it had nearly five hundred freemen but is now much reduced in size, having lost its industrial function. Its hall was built in 1471 and, somewhat altered, is one of Exeter's architectural treasures

The manufacture of handmade or Honiton lace was widely distributed through east Devon in the eighteenth century but this trade declined under the impact of competition from machine-made lace of which the leading manufacturer became Heathcoats. John Heathcoat established a lace factory at Tiverton in 1816 and another was opened at Barnstaple in 1822.

Carpet manufacture was established at Axminster in 1755 by Thomas Whitty, a clothier who saw a Turkey carpet in London, copied it on one of his weaving looms that April and began manufacture in June. The first carpet was ordered by a Mr Cook of Slape near Beaminster but in fact went to the Earl of Shaftesbury when completed. Other customers included the Sultan of Turkey! In 1757-8 Whitty shared prizes offered by the Society of Arts and in 1759 obtained the sole premium of £30 for the largest and most handsome carpet made in this country up to that time. Whitty's descendants continued the business until 1835 when the looms were taken to Wilton. Almost a century later in the 1930s the industry was revived in new premises on the outskirts of Axminster with the help of workers from Kidderminster and still continues.

Higher Mill, Buckfast, was built as a woollen mill in the early nineteenth century. It has a slate-hung front and, along the rear, as shown in this photograph, a wooden launder was used to convey water to the waterwheel. This building is now used by a metal-plating company

When the wool was brought to the woollen mill it had to be sorted into different grades for particular types of cloth. Here is shown wool sorting at the Newton Abbot firm of John Vicary & Sons Ltd in the 1920s. This firm ceased production in 1971

The serge factory at Ottery St. Mary, photographed here in 1948, was built by John Duntze and Sir George Yonge in the 1790s to revive the dwindling wool trade of the town. In 1815 it contained two combing machines, 8 sliver-drawing and roving frames, 59 spinning-frames, 34 warping bars, one twisting frame, one fluting engine and 6 reels or skaines. However, serge-making was not successful here and in 1823 the building was converted into a silk factory. It is now occupied by an electronics firm

One of the processes of wool preparation is carding to align the fibres of the wool. This carding machine was formerly in a woollen mill at Weare Giffard. It was later taken to Torrington and adapted for the manufacture of flock mattresses

The upper floors of woollen mills were often used as wool stores. One of the few remaining stores is this wooden-sided loft in Ashburton, once a flourishing wool town

Raw wool is combed by either the noble combing system, in the case of long-fibred yarns destined for use in worsted cloth, or the French or rectilinear combing system for wool destined for woollen garments. This photograph shows noble combing at Vicarys at Newton Abbot

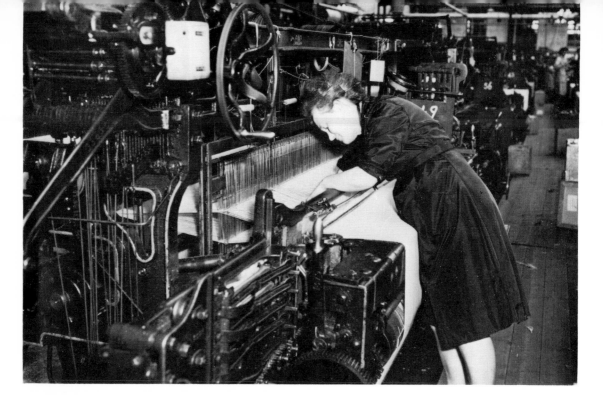

Once the wool has been prepared and spun, it is made into cloth by weaving. This photograph shows one of the modern looms in the weaving shed in one of the few woollen mills in Devon which is still working, at Buckfastleigh

This Plymouth halfpenny was issued by Shepheard Dove Hammett & Company's hemp and flax manufactory which was founded by eight men as a philanthropic venture to give employment to the poor, making sailcloth—one of the staple trades of Plymouth. The same picture was used on tokens in other parts of the country

Machine-made lace was introduced into Devon when John Heathcoat moved from Loughborough to Tiverton in 1816 into a factory which was originally built as a cottonmill by Heathfield and Dennis in 1791. This factory has now been replaced by a modern one but the firm retains this model of the bobinette lace machine which Heathcoat invented in 1803 and improved and patented in 1809

The only example of early industrial architecture in north Devon is the Barnstaple Derby lace factory, built about 1822 for the production of machine-made lace and net. It continued to make net until August 1970 and then produced man-made textiles for shirts and lingerie until damaged by fire in 1972

The building where Whitty first began making carpets in Axminster in 1755 burnt down in the autumn of 1826 or 1827 and larger premises were built in the centre of the town close to the church, consisting of three plain stone buildings, one of which is seen here

A view of the broadloom section of the present facory, which occupies a different site on the outskirts of Axminster, showing a 12ft wide jacquard loom

Paper

The earliest papermill in Devon was started at Countess Wear, Exeter in 1638 but the industry did not expand significantly until a century or so later. Then, taking advantage of the plentiful supplies of water for power and manufacture, and the supplies of cloth waste which could be used as raw material, a number of works were set up in the Creedy and Culm valleys to the north of Exeter and in the neighbourhood of Plymouth. By the end of the eighteenth century there were 30 mills in the county (out of a total of 425 mills in England and Wales). Some of the mills took over the buildings vacated when clothmaking ceased and employed some of the workers. In terms of separate works, the industry reached its peak in the 1830s when forty-seven papermills were in operation. Thereafter factories closed as the adoption of the new Fourdrinier process and steam-power hastened concentration. By 1910 there were ten mills and today only four papermills are operating in Devon. Though some good quality writing and printing paper was produced in the nineteenth century, most of the Devon output consisted of common wrapping paper. Nowadays a wide range of papers is produced in the county.

Head Weir papermill in Exeter was powered by water-driven turbines, the water actually coming from the adjacent Blackaller Weir, with an auxiliary steam engine until it closed in July 1967. A fulling mill formerly occupied the site but this was converted to papermaking in 1787. Corn was also milled here for a time. The mill was rebuilt and re-equipped after a serious fire in 1882

A major raw material for paper was rags. Here rags are seen being sorted at Hele Mill. The coarser and more deeply-coloured rags were used for inferior quality paper

To convert the rags into pulp they were soaked and boiled in large circular boilers

The Hollander beater, so called because it was invented in Holland, was adopted in this country from the mid-eighteenth century. It is used to macerate the rags into pulp

The Fourdrinier machine formed the paper on an endless belt of woven wire, replacing the separate moulds of the handmade process. It was invented in France at the end of the eighteenth century but did not become common until the 1830s and thereafter. This photograph shows the 'wet' end, the beginning of the machine where the fibres are formed into a sheet of paper

The Devon Valley papermill at Hele was established in 1762 and took over part of a flour mill. It was burnt down and rebuilt in 1821 and shortly after this the waterwheel was replaced by steam power and a turbine and machines were installed, although handmade paper continued to be produced until 1853. The mill now belongs to the Wiggins Teape group who purchased it in 1920

The interior of the Devon Valley mill today contains more modern machinery than that illustrated on the previous pages but the principles of paper manufacture have not altered, as is seen in this picture of the 'dry' end of one of their Fourdrinier machines. At this end of the machine the sheet of paper is dried on heated rollers

Mills and Milling

Water and wind power have both been extensively used to drive mills in Devon as well as to supply the power for other types of industry. Waterwheels were commonly of two types— the overshot wheel where the water, carried to the top of the wheel by a launder, drives the wheel from above; and the undershot wheel which is driven by the force of the water imping- ing against the lower vanes of the wheel. Other possible variations are the pitchback wheel, described on page 23, and high or low breasted wheels in which the water hits the wheel above or below the centre point.

Contrary to previous belief, windmills were also common in Devon; at present 28 definite and another 20 possible sites are known and in nine cases there are surviving remains. Windmills may be post mills, the earliest form, in which the mill is built largely of wood on a stone or trestle base and the whole mill turns to face the wind; smock mills, also built of wood with a cap which rotates to face the wind; or tower mills, the type which most often survives, which are built of brick or stone and also have a rotating cap.

Of lesser importance were tidemills which once existed in all the major estuaries in the county. Usually built near the mouth of a tidal inlet, the tidemill was driven by the power of the water turning a wheel in the channel through which it escaped as the tide ebbed. Tidemills were less common because the changing times and heights of the tides prevented continuous or regular working, but at least thirteen are known to have existed in Devon. The earliest reference is a lease for the Dartmouth town mills in 1250 but many of them date from the nineteenth century.

Stoke Gabriel tidemill is shown on the 1840 tithe map and in 1850 William White described the village 'where a small creek . . . being dammed up is made to turn the wheel of a tidal cornmill'. As this drawing by William Payne of about 1793 shows, there were two millhouses, each with its own wheel, on the dam. Today the build- ings have disappeared but the dam survives and the position of the millhouses is clear

A source of power which was more common in Devon in the past than has been recognised up to now is wind. Above is the remains of the tower of North Whilborough windmill, near Newton Abbot. Built of red sandstone, it probably dates from the late eighteenth century and went out of use in about the 1830s. A windmill which no longer exists, that at Exmouth, is shown in the 1829 lithograph by Frédéric Martens below. It was built in 1797 at a cost of £300 but by 1829 it was driven from inside, probably by a horse or donkey, and it also ceased to operate in the 1830s

A pitchback wheel which used to drive a grist mill is this 30ft diameter cast-iron wheel at Dawlish, built by A. Bodley of Exeter. The launder bringing the water to drive the wheel can be seen in the left of the picture. The water poured onto the wheel at a point where it made the wheel turn in an anti-clockwise direction, as seen in this picture. An ordinary overshot wheel would turn in a clockwise direction, seen from this position

A low-breasted wheel can be seen at what is now known as Riverside Mill, Bovey Tracey. The building, dating from 1854, was in fact built as a coach house and the wheel was used for pumping water up to a slate tank on top of the tower to supply Riverside, or Bridge, House, owned by John Divett, and to water the gardens and stable yard. The building now belongs to Standard Telephone & Cables Ltd

This gypsum mill, for the manufacture of plaster of paris from gypsum found in the cliffs and on the shore nearby, was built on the beach at Branscombe by a Mr Wheaton of Exeter about 1855. Never a commercial success, due to its distance from the railway and the uncertainty of sea transport on this treacherous coast, it had closed by the end of the nineteenth century. The overshot iron-rimmed wheel, driving the grinding machinery, was about 12ft in diameter

The mill at Jacobstow, now a sawmill, has two wheels alongside each other. Another example of this arrangement still exists at Otterton

The interior of Ashburton Town Mills showing the millstones enclosed in circular wooden boxes and the crown wheel which drove the secondary machinery in the mill, such as the sack hoist. The date of the mill is unknown but it was last worked in 1962 and the premises were then used by a coal merchant for six years. At present all the machinery remains in the mill but it is threatened with destruction

Dressing the millstones to ensure even grinding to the required fineness was a skilled job. This craftsman was photographed at work at Bidlake mill in 1969

This tumbling weir at Ottery St Mary serge factory (see page 12) took the excess water not required to drive the waterwheel under the mill buildings and back to the river. It is unique in Devon and only one or two examples exist in the rest of the country

Brewing, Cider and Gin

In Devon, as in other parts of England, breweries were small in size and widely distributed throughout the county but in this century, and particularly since 1945, the pressure has been for concentration. In 1890, for example, there were fifteen breweries in Exeter but today there are none.

For hundreds of years cider has been made on farms using hand or horse presses. Defoe noted that between Topsham and Axminster 'they have so vast a quantity of fruit and so much cider that sometimes they sent twenty thousand hogsheads a year to London'. In the nineteenth century cider also formed an important part of the wages of agricultural labourers. The old method still survives on a number of farms but from about 1890 commercial making began and a number of cideries were set up.

Gin was introduced into this country about 300 years ago and rapidly became very popular as a cheap form of spirits which the poorest could afford. Though less widespread than brewing, gin distilling was carried on in many large towns. Since the nineteenth century manufacture has become concentrated in a few places, of which Plymouth is one.

Parts of this malthouse in Bartholomew Street East, Exeter, date from the sixteenth century and the kiln was built by H. J. H. King & Co of Nailsworth, Glos. In the late nineteenth century it passed to St Anne's Well Brewery (see page 31) and continued in use until 1966. The building has now been converted into a restaurant but the kiln remains

The Anchor Brewery in Plymouth, seen here from the bridge, was one of five breweries which amalgamated in 1888 to form Plymouth Breweries

Ford's brewery at Tiverton was founded in 1852. The business rapidly expanded and it moved into larger premises in 1857, further expanding them in 1859. The brewery is now owned by Starkey, Knight & Ford Ltd, a member of the Whitbread Group. Here we see a malting floor in the west maltings drawn in the 1880s

Two more drawings of Ford's brewery in the 1880s show the interior of the brewhouse (above) and the mild ale cellar and union room (below)

Heavitree Brewery was the last brewery to operate in Exeter; it closed in 1970. Until the end it had a coopery where wooden barrels were made by hand but the cooper seen here is the last of his family to take up the craft as wooden barrels are being replaced by steel ones

St Anne's Well Brewery in Exeter is an impressive Victorian building. There was a maltings on the site in 1830 and the main brewery buildings originated about 1879 and were expanded in the 1890s. It takes its name from St Anne's Well, higher up the Longbrook valley in which it is situated, from whence it drew its water. The brewery became redundant in the recent brewery amalgamations and the building is now owned by a printing firm. The silhouette in the foreground is the iron bridge (see page 79)

These brewery workers were photographed at the brewery at Warfleet, Dartmouth. The premises is now the Dartmouth Pottery

Coates gin distillery in Plymouth was established in 1783 in premises (above) believed to contain the oldest surviving building in the city—the fourteenth-century refectory of the Dominican friary; on the left of the photograph below can be seen a pot-still dating from 1855 and a rectifying still of 1856

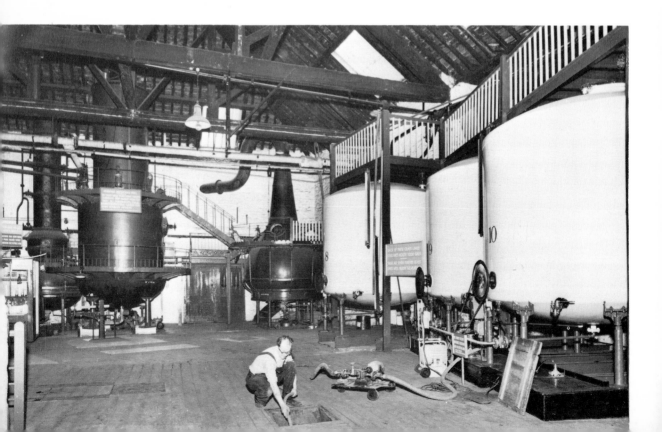

Cider making in Devon in the nineteenth century. This drawing shows the poundhouse containing a horsemill on the right, which is used to grind the apples before they are put into the cider press, shown on the left

A typical west country horse-driven granite cider mill as used on farms

Today, while cider is still made on a number of farms, it is made commercially on a much larger scale. This modern press is at the Teign Cider Company's works at Netherton, near Shaldon

The huge vats of the Teign Cider Company give some impression of the scale of operation

Ford's brewery at Tiverton also produced mineral waters and here we see the interior of the factory which was built and equipped in the 1880s

Quarrying and Limekilns

Throughout the county, which is rich in various types of stone, quarrying has gone on for centuries. In the east, Beer stone, a chalk stone; in the Exeter area, Exeter traps, volcanic stone; on Dartmoor, granite at Blackingstone, Haytor, Merrivale and Walkhampton; in the south of Devon, between Plymouth and Chudleigh, the extensive mining of limestone; near Kingsbridge, slate; and in the Tavistock area, green trappear ash stone; these are but some of the stones which have been quarried for building purposes. Each has contributed to the distinctive appearance of the houses, churches and other buildings in its locality, while the granite and limestone have also been carried further afield.

From at least the sixteenth century lime was burnt to spread on the land to reduce the acidity of Devon soil. Remains of limekilns are to be found along the north and south coasts of Devon and on the banks of the Tamar, Kingsbridge, Exe and Torridge estuaries. In the south the limekilns were supplied mainly from local quarries but in the north the greater part of the limestone came from south Wales. From the beginning of this century local production of lime declined in the face of competition from large-scale mechanised lime-crushing works and artificial fertilisers.

Slate was obtained from Cann or Carn Quarry in Bickleigh Vale

Extensive limestone quarries at Beer have been worked since Roman times. They were most active in the fifteenth and sixteenth centuries but declined with the cessation of church building. Stone from the quarries was used extensively in Exeter Cathedral and a large number of east Devon churches. Now they are only used for extracting lime unless stone is needed for particular repair purposes. The upper photograph shows the quarries in the 1900s and below is a view of the interior of the workings showing the wide pillars that were left and the narrow seam of good quality stone

The Yeo Vale limekiln on the river Torridge, south-west of Bideford, is a particularly splendid example with a castellated top and gothic arches

This kiln at Cockwood, Dawlish Warren, is one of the many still to be found in south Devon

On the coast of north Devon between Westward Ho! and Clovelly are Bucks Mills limekilns. The limestone and coal from south Wales was brought by vessels which stood on hards on the beach and unloaded via a gangplank arrangement. The burnt lime was carried up this inclined plane and then transported to the farms where it was used. The kilns were abandoned at the beginning of this century but have recently been restored

There were several limekilns on the Rolle canal (see page 82). They are now in ruins but this plan of what they must have looked like in their heyday has been constructed with the help of old photographs

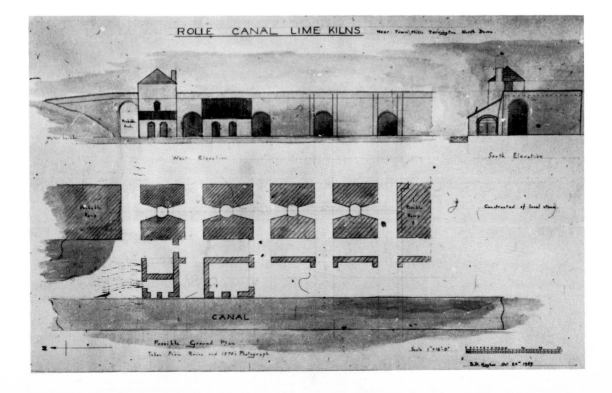

Some of the Devon limestone is hard enough to take a polish and is known as 'Ashburton marble', which was widely exported. It used to be quarried in a number of places in the Plymouth and Torquay areas and the Ashburton quarry worked until 1970. The upper photograph shows the head of the wire saw, used to cut blocks of up to 10 tons off the face of the quarry, being adjusted for use; below is a close-up of a sawing head

The Haytor granite quarries were very active in the first half of the nineteenth century. For a period several thousands of tons of granite were quarried each year and was used for such famous buildings as the British Museum and the National Gallery. In 1850 the quarries were employing about 100 men but by 1858 they had closed, due largely to competition from coastal quarries in Cornwall which were easier to work and had cheaper transport facilities. This engraving probably dates from the 1820s. It shows the cranes for lifting the blocks of granite and one of the flat trucks used on the granite tramway (see page 89)

Mining

Mining tin, copper, lead and other ores has been a source of wealth in Devon for many centuries. There are three main areas: north Devon, Dartmoor and the Tamar valley. In north Devon most of the working was on a small scale with copper and iron being produced at North Molton, silver and lead at Combe Martin and manganese at Upton Pyne and Newton St Cyres, near Exeter, and in west Devon. Dartmoor was a more important mining area. The peak period for tin was in the middle ages but some mining continued in the nineteenth century, the largest mines being Wheal Betsy and Wheal Friendship, both near Mary Tavy, which produced copper, lead and tin. By 1914 most of the mining on the moor had come to an end but there were some arsenic workings in the 1920s and the last tin was obtained from a small working near Postbridge in the 1930s. The mining of barites was carried on at Bridford until 1956 and micaceous haematite, a paint compound, was produced until recently at Hennock. The most important mining area was the Tamar valley and the major metal worked there was copper. This mining developed in the Tavistock area at the end of the eighteenth century and the peak of copper production was reached in 1862 but thereafter output declined fairly sharply. The Tamar valley also produced tin, iron, lead, silver, fluorspar, uranium, wolfram and arsenic.

Ramsley Mine, South Zeal, worked from about 1850 to 1880 and again for a few years in the early twentieth century, producing copper. Note the waterwheel and the inclined plane by which the ore was conveyed to the crushing and sorting sheds

One of the most dramatic remains of the mining industry in Devon is the engine house of Wheal Betsy, north of Mary Tavy, which produced lead, silver and zinc. An old mine, it was restarted in 1806 and again reopened in 1863 under the name of Prince Arthur Consols. The engine house was built in 1868 and the mine closed about 1877. As the plaque below shows, it is now preserved by the National Trust

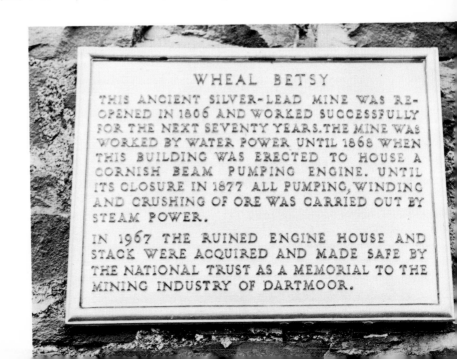

WHEAL BETSY

THIS ANCIENT SILVER-LEAD MINE WAS RE-OPENED IN 1806 AND WORKED SUCCESSFULLY FOR THE NEXT SEVENTY YEARS. THE MINE WAS WORKED BY WATER POWER UNTIL 1868 WHEN THIS BUILDING WAS ERECTED TO HOUSE A CORNISH BEAM PUMPING ENGINE. UNTIL ITS CLOSURE IN 1877 ALL PUMPING, WINDING AND CRUSHING OF ORE WAS CARRIED OUT BY STEAM POWER.

IN 1967 THE RUINED ENGINE HOUSE AND STACK WERE ACQUIRED AND MADE SAFE BY THE NATIONAL TRUST AS A MEMORIAL TO THE MINING INDUSTRY OF DARTMOOR.

The waterwheel used for draining the mine at Wheal Maria, Devon Great Consols, about 1937

The stamps for crushing tin ore and the waterwheel at Golden Dagger mine, near Postbridge on Dartmoor in 1937. This mine was worked from 1879 and in prosperous times employed between thirty and forty men

Little Duke, a tin and copper mine in the Tamar valley near Buckland Monachorum, showing miners on the old stope above the 20 fathom level during the time when the mine was reworked for arsenic early in this century. Note the candles used for illumination, a practice which greatly increased the risks of explosion

Tavy Consols Mine during its last period of working for arsenic. The ruins at the top of the dumps in the background are on the site of the nineteenth-century ore crushing mill. Also to be seen are the round frames used for separating the mineral from the waste after the ore has been crushed by washing the waste into the centre of the revolving frame

Barites, a soft white mineral occuring in granite and used in the nineteenth century chiefly for producing hydrogen peroxide, was mined at La Porte mine, Bridford. This photograph shows some of the surface equipment used for conveying the mineral from the shaft head to railway trucks at Christow station

Mining at North Molton was carried on in the middle ages and developed at the end of the seventeenth century when Cornish miners were brought in to work the mines for copper and iron. These north Devon mines were last worked in 1942 when they were opened to meet war needs. One of the most important mines in this complex was Bamfylde, shown here in about 1875

Above is a narrow lode of micaceous haematite in Great Rock mine, Hennock, and below is the interior of the crushing mill at the mine showing the crushed ore being passed through tubs and sluices to remove the waste. In operation from the 1840s to the 1880s and again from 1902 to 1969, Great Rock was the last working metalliferous mine in Devon. Its output, a type of iron oxide, was used in the manufacture of non-corrosive paints

Attempts to find coal in Devon were made near Exeter in 1698, in the 1760s and in 1818 but all were unsuccessful. Subsequently coal was mined at Bovey Heathfield to supply the potteries of Bovey Tracey. Until 1970 a mine, shown here, remained in operation at Bideford. In the nineteenth century it produced a special anthracite for lime kilns and later a black pigment used in paint making was mined there

Wolfram, a tungsten mineral, was worked at Hemerdon Ball, Plympton, during and immediately following the two world wars; in the early twentieth century, working was opencast alone but later shafts were also used. This photograph shows the opencast workings and the mill capable of treating 300 tons of ore a day

The only remains of the silver-lead mines at Combe Martin, once a source of great wealth, are this ruined engine-house chimney and a number of shafts and adits. The history of the mines dates back to the late thirteenth century when 337 men were brought from Derbyshire to work them. They were last operated about 90 years ago

When this drawing by Frederick Foot of Silverbrook Mine near Ilsington on Dartmoor was made in the nineteenth century, the mine was already said to have been working for 200 years. It produced lead and zinc ore and silver and it employed 60 people in 1857. It was closed about four years later. From left to right, the buildings shown are the count house, the material house and blacksmith shop, the dressing house attached to the engine-house and the crushing house to the right of the shaft and headgear

Clay and Associated Products

China clay, produced by the kaolinisation of granite, is found at Lee Moor on the south-west of Dartmoor. It was originally exploited by William Cookworthy of Plymouth in the 1760s to make porcelain but now finds its way into many articles including paper, cosmetics, paint, rubber and medicines. Ball clay, obtained in the Bovey Tracey area in south Devon and at Fremington and Peters Marland in north Devon, was formerly important for tobacco pipes and is now used for pottery. Much ball clay is exported for use elsewhere.

Bricks were first used in Devon in the sixteenth century but were uncommon until the nineteenth century. By the end of the century there were numerous small brickworks in the county, mainly supplying local needs, but since 1920 the rationalisation of the industry has caused the closure of most of them and the expansion of a few. For example, at the turn of the century there were at least sixteen brickworks in east Devon and of these only two are still operating.

Clay is also used for pottery. Some potteries in the county trace their origins back to the eighteenth century but all have changed hands a number of times since then. Today the manufacture of common ware has been supplemented by the production of fancy domestic pottery.

A view of Southacre pit, Newton Abbot, showing the method of excavating ball clay which continued into the 1930s. The clay was dug out with picks and shovels. A stream of water then passed over it, carrying with it the solid material. The heavy sand and mica was removed in settling pits and the suspension of clay continued to catchment pits or ponds where it settled out and the water was removed

Today ball clay in open-cast pits is extracted by a rotary cutter and transferred by a moving belt straight to the truck for transport from the workings, as shown here

Here men are seen working underground at the Kingsteignton ball clay works

The centre of the china clay industry is in the St Austell area of Cornwall but some china clay is mined in Devon. This is a view of Lee Moor showing the china clay workings and clay heaps

In September 1858 the Lee Moor Tramway was opened to carry the clay down to Plymouth for distribution. This crossed the main South Devon Railway line at Laira junction, seen here in 1933. Steam, gravity and horse traction were used on different parts of the line

One use of ball clay is for making earthenware pipes and this photograph shows the pipe-firing ovens at Heathfield pottery, Newton Abbot

Lee Moor brick and tile works, which used the refuse from the china clay pits, showing the kilns, drying and mixing sheds and the grading and mixing plant. The brickworks was established on this site at Torycombe outside Lee Moor village in the 1850s and closed in 1943. The premises now house plant processing flake mica

In 1768 William Cookworthy of Plymouth took out the first British patent for making porcelain in the oriental style. His Plymouth factory had closed by the end of 1770 and he had moved to Bristol, but one of the finest pieces produced at Plymouth was the Putto and Dolphin shown here

Pottery in Torrington Lane, East-the-Water, Bideford, which closed in 1917, photographed just before the buildings were demolished in 1920

The first stage in pottery making was preparing the clay to be moulded or thrown. This process is here seen at Longpark Pottery in the 1920s. This pottery occupied the unused atmospheric railway engine house at Torre (see page 87)

Manpower for driving the potters' machinery at Longpark Pottery

Forming a pot on a steampowered wheel at Longpark Pottery

Part of the making department at Honiton pottery in 1935. In the foreground can be seen a potter's wheel and a machine for shaping the inside of pots and similar articles. Behind the man are some moulds for making jugs etc. The women workers in this department are smoothing the inside of the jugs. Behind them another worker is stacking the pottery to dry before firing

Green's china shop, High Street, Bideford in 1887; now Lloyds Bank occupies this corner. This large shop sold all kinds of china and local north Devon pottery as can be seen from the display in its window and outside

Ports and Harbours

The sea has been very important for the economy of Devon. In the seventeenth and eighteenth centuries Devon was prominent in the Atlantic trades. Barnstaple and Bideford took part in the tobacco trade with Virginia and Maryland; Exeter had an appreciable trade with the Carolinas and the West Indies although as the chief cloth port its main links were with Europe; Dartmouth was the most important Devon port in the triangular trade with Newfoundland and the Mediterranean. There were also flourishing trades with Ireland, south Wales, Bristol, London and Newcastle, and alongside peaceful commerce was the growth in importance of Plymouth as a naval base from which warships could operate in the western English Channel. During the nineteenth century these trades reached a peak and then declined with the development of large vessels and the steamship.

As well as the Newfoundland fisheries, fishing took place from Devon ports in home waters for the British market. The pilchard fishery was carried on from south Devon ports in the eighteenth century but declined in the early nineteenth century. Herring and mackerel fishery continued longer but these too went into a decline later in the century. Today there is some mackerel fishing on a small scale from various Devon ports and a greatly diminished trawler fleet operating from Brixham.

An important trade for many of the north Devon ports was the import of limestone and coal from south Wales to supply the many limekilns along the coast. This photograph shows limestone being unloaded at Ilfracombe about 1880. The limekiln at Clovelly can be seen in the photograph on page 65

This view of Exeter quay was drawn in the 1830s, soon after the completion of the bonded warehouses to be seen on the right. These warehouses, which still exist, were built on land leased from the city. The one on the left, built of limestone with red sandstone dressing, has the date 1835 and the name of Mayor de la Garde inscribed on it and was probably built by Robert Stribling Cornish while the red stone one on the right was built by William, Henry and William Wills Hooper in or soon after 1835. The picture also shows the ferry across the Exe and gives an impression of how busy the port was at this time

The quay at Topsham about 1870 showing the house of the Quay Master and the King's weigh-beam which was used by the Customs officers for weighing dutiable goods. It is one of the few which still remain in the country

There are a number of lighthouses along the north and south coasts of Devon, as at Hartland Point and Berry Head, and smaller lighthouses also mark the entrances to harbours. This miniature lighthouse at the far end of the Den in Teignmouth was built in 1845

An inland port is Morwellham on the river Tamar, 23 miles up river from Plymouth at the highest point to which vessels of 10ft draught could navigate the tidal river. It was the port for Tavistock from the middle ages but its period of prosperity came when the copper mines at Devon Great Consols boomed in the 1850s. In 1859 a new dock was built at a cost of £5000 and this is one of the granite bollards which stood on the dockside. But the copper was soon exhausted and by the 1870s the port was hardly used. Today the quays and the dock with its bollards remain together with a number of partly ruined buildings and the site is being developed as an amenity centre

At Teignmouth a different story can be told. The basis of this port's trade is the ball clay industry which is still flourishing so the port remains busy and prosperous. Here ball clay can be seen being loaded by chute onto a vessel for export

Dartmouth Custom House, built in 1739, and two of the houses in Bayard's Cove, a seventeenth-century group of waterfront houses

This splendid lifeboat house at South Sands, Salcombe, was built in 1877-8; it was endowed by the United Grand Lodge of Freemasons of England and stands on land given by Lord Devon for the original wooden house built in 1869. It remained in use until the station was closed in 1925. Since the station was reopened in 1930 the motor lifeboat has been kept afloat on moorings in the estuary

Clovelly is a typical example of the many small fishing villages around the Devon coast; note the old limekiln (on right) now used as a boat house

The quay and pier at Lynmouth were built in the eighteenth century for the herring fishery, and the so-called Rhenish tower was erected about 1860 by a General Rawdon to store salt water for indoor baths. This photograph was taken in 1900

The *Privateer*, a Swansea paddlesteamer, ran pleasure trips from Bideford to other Bristol Channel ports in the 1880s. This photograph was taken before 1889–90 when the quay was widened to its present extent. A sailing barge can be seen behind the steamer and the Steam Packet & Railway Hotel and the Newfoundland Hotel are significantly named after important sources of income in the town

In Devon, inshore fishing was done by means of a seine net, one end of which was fastened on the shore while the other end was taken out to sea and then drawn in enclosing the fish, as can be seen here

Lobsters are a well-known Devon speciality and the fishermen, like this Clovelly man and his sons photographed in the late nineteenth century, spend the slack season, late winter and early spring, making their lobster pots for next year

Brixham is the most important fishing port in Devon with a noted market. This photograph shows the harbour in about 1880 with some of the fishing vessels

In the mid-nineteenth century, Plymouth was the second fishing port and its fish market was held on the Barbican, here photographed in the 1900s

Shipbuilding

Linked with the maritime trade of the county was shipbuilding. This was carried on at many of the Devon ports such as Exmouth, Brixham, Dartmouth, Plymouth, Appledore and Bideford. Particularly in the middle of the nineteenth century, yards in the county were busy building schooners, but various factors led to the decline of shipbuilding and now, apart from the construction of pleasure craft and naval building, little shipbuilding, and that only on a small scale, takes place except at Appledore and Dartmouth.

Today the naval dockyard at Devonport is the most important branch of the industry. This dates from the end of the seventeenth century when work first began on the building of docks and associated facilities; the wars of the eighteenth century led to a rapid expansion of the naval establishment. It remained important in the nineteenth century and it is only recently that it has begun to contract.

Ancillary to shipbuilding were other activities such as ropemaking and sailmaking. These trades, too, have declined but in ports like Bideford, Plymouth and Topsham the evidence of ropewalks and sail-lofts can still be seen.

Dartmouth has been a considerable shipbuilding town and an important landmark in its history was the building of Sand Quay shipyard by John Seale in 1795. The largest man-of-war to be built in Dartmouth, the 36-gun frigate *Dartmouth* of 952 tons, was built in this yard in 1813. This engraving shows the graving dock, sawmills, store houses, dwelling houses etc in 1845 when the yard belonged to Captain I. R. Pidding

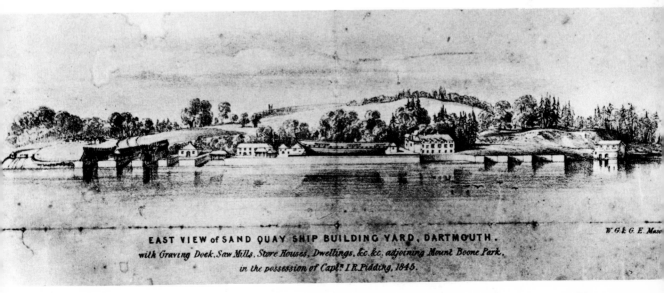

EAST VIEW of SAND QUAY SHIP BUILDING YARD, DARTMOUTH.
with Graving Dock, Saw Mills, Store Houses, Dwellings, &c.&c. adjoining Mount Boone Park,
in the possession of Capt.ⁿ I R Pidding, 1845.

The biggest firm of shipbuilders in Topsham was Holmans who, in 1842, took over the Upper Yard—the most important in the town—which had been in use since 1800. They installed a large patent slipway for lifting vessels here in 1850. The yard, which was originally twice as long as it appears in this modern photograph, was used commercially until 1860, employing up to 200 men, and during its active life over 100 vessels of 100 to 300 tons were built here

Appledore was a busy shipbuilding centre for many years. In the middle of the nineteenth century William Yeo built the 330ft long Richmond Dry Dock (1855), chiefly to complete vessels built in Prince Edward Island, and brought to England for the final stages of construction and sale, and improved the three existing shipyards. The port continued to build, mainly wooden vessels, up until the 1940s. This photograph shows the first steamer to be repaired in Richmond Dry Dock in 1906

Reputedly the last vessel to be built by Holmans on the slip shown on page 70 is this 97-ton topsail schooner, the *Myth*, painted here at her launching in 1856. She was a short-lived vessel and was stranded and sold in about 1859

Ship repair as well as shipbuilding was carried on in Devon ports. Here the ketch *Acacia* (Captain Ben Rogers) is being caulked with pitch at Appledore in 1902

Drawings showing the method of rope-making by hand: 1 combing the hemp; 2 spinning two yarns; 3 making a rope of three strands (*a* top, *b* yarns being warped); 4 tarring a rope; 5 top for positioning the strands of the rope as shown in drawing 3

The Strand ropewalk, one of three in Bideford, closed in 1886 and was replaced by a collar factory. The ropes were stretched around these posts all the way down the Strand and many of them remained for some years after the works closed as the local inhabitants protested at their removal

A modern sail-loft at the naval dockyard in Devonport. The sailmakers' long stools with holes at one end to hold the awls, mallets and hooks that they used, and the posts and tackle for holding the sails taut so that the necessary rope-work could be attached, have altered little over the years

Roads

The increase in traffic in the eighteenth century led to the improvement of the roads once a general turnpike act was passed. The London road from Exeter was turnpiked by the Exeter, Honiton and Axminster Trust in 1753 and trusts to develop other main roads were set up soon after. In some cases entirely new roads were constructed to by-pass the villages on the way as, for example, between Crediton and Barnstaple. John Macadam was employed by some of the trusts and his method of surfacing roads greatly improved conditions. By 1850 virtually the present network of roads had been constructed. Tollhouses were built to collect the tolls levied for the use of the new road system and along with road improvement went the construction of new bridges.

The need for improved public transport in the towns led to the development of tram and bus services. The first horsedrawn tram ran in Plymouth in 1872 and Exeter followed ten years later; electric trams appeared in Plymouth in 1899, in Exeter in 1905 and in Torquay in 1907. But the trams could not compete with the buses which coped better with the narrow Devon roads and could serve country areas. The last Exeter tram ran in 1931 and in Torquay the service closed in 1934 while in Plymouth they survived until 1945. After the first bus service was started in 1904 they increased slowly until 1914 when many of the buses were commandeered for war use; after 1919 the network grew quickly and was virtually complete by 1939. Today, as the private car takes over more and more of the country traffic, bus routes are again being reduced and even urban services are declining.

Seaton bridge, 1877, is believed to be the second concrete bridge to be built in England and the oldest surviving. It was designed by Philip Brannon for Sir W. C. Trevelyan, Lord of the Manor of Seaton. The original design of a single 100ft arch frightened the Board of Trade and a design of three arches was substituted. It has simulated joints as if built of masonry

This tollhut is at Yealmbridge on the main road from Plymouth to Modbury. Nearby there is also a tollhouse and it has been suggested that this was associated with the bridge over the Yealm and that the hut was erected later, around 1824, in connection with the proposed new road linking Yealmpton and Ermington. Another theory is that the hut was erected to catch the local farmers who joined the toll road from a sideroad without passing the toll-house

Tolls were charged for bridges as well as for roads. The tollhouse at the north end of the original Shaldon bridge was erected in 1827 and continued to collect tolls into the 1930s. The building still stands minus its porch. This photograph was taken in 1943

This drawing of Withy Bridge Gate in Exeter in 1884 gives some impression of what tollhouses looked like in their heyday. Note the porch for the toll collector to stand illuminated by a large lamp, the wooden gates to close across the road when the cart has gone through and the small gate at the side of the road for pedestrians

Honiton once had seven tollhouses guarding its entrances but the only one now remaining is that on the Axminster road. Its unusual battlemented design caused it to be called the 'copper castle'. It is the only Devon tollhouse retaining its original wrought iron gates, although as a result of subsequent road widening they would no longer meet in the middle when closed

The turnpike trusts were required to erect milestones along their roads to direct travellers and indicate how far they had to travel. The design of these milestones was very varied: some were incised stone; some had cast-iron plates bearing the lettering; some were entirely of iron. This particularly splendid example can be seen in a wall out of Exeter and one of its companions remains in situ, but somewhat sunk into the ground, further along the road

On steep hills heavily laden waggons or coaches could add an extra toll-free horse to help pull the vehicle up the hill but this horse had to be removed at the top of the hill. This 'Take-off' stone at Beardon near Lydford is one of the few such stones remaining in the country, marking the point where the extra horse had to be removed

Another statutory obligation on the turnpike trusts was the erection of parish boundary posts where their roads crossed a boundary. A number of these remain throughout Devon. This example can be seen on Woodbury Common

During the eighteenth century the number of coaching routes in Devon increased and some of them survived into the twentieth century. This photograph, taken before the first world war, shows the stage coach Lorna Doone about to ascend Countisbury Hill, for which it needed two extra horses, on its daily journey to Minehead. It was painted red, black and gold and the driver and guard wore red coats with brass buttons

A splendid example of an early iron bridge is the North Road iron bridge in Exeter which was built in 1834-5 at the expense of the Improvement Commissioners and spans the Longbrook valley. It has six cast iron arches of 40ft span and carries a roadway 24ft wide; the overall length of the bridge, including the masonry approaches, is 800ft. The inscription, seen above, reads 'Russell & Browns Blaina Iron Works 1834'. Although Blaina is in Monmouthshire, Russell & Brown are said to have been a Worcester firm

A five-horse tramcar at Halfpenny Gate, Plymouth

Bideford to Barnstaple bus photographed soon after the service started in 1923-4. It used both the coastal route and the old road through Westleigh and also served the country districts on the way

Exeter's electric tramway system was constructed between 1903 and 1905 and was inaugurated in the April of the latter year. It closed down in 1931. The trams were an important factor in linking the suburbs of St Thomas and Heavitree with the city. On the right is one of the control boxes for the trams which remained at the side of the road by the Exe bridge until early 1971 when it was destroyed by the building of the new bridge. Below is an electric tram at the top of Sidwell Street soon after the system started

Canals

Canals were built in Devon to supplement roads and rivers for the transport of heavy goods, mainly ores, stone, coal, lime and sand. Some were improvements or alternatives to existing rivers and others were designed to bring cheap water transport to areas where it was not naturally available. The Exeter Ship Canal, built in the 1560s, was the first in the country to have genuine pound locks. It subsequently underwent several improvements and by 1827 could take vessels of up to 400 tons. The rest of the canal history of the county is compressed into the half century after 1790. The Stover canal to carry clay from Teigngrace was opened in 1795, the Tamar was improved in 1808, the Tavistock canal, linking the mines in the district to Morwellham quay, was built between 1803 and 1817 with a branch to Mill Hill quarry by 1819. In north Devon, the Bude canal was constructed between 1819 and 1825. The six-mile Torrington or Rolle Canal was built in 1823–5 at a cost of about £40,000 linking Torrington and Bideford, chiefly to carry south Wales limestone from Appledore and Bideford to Lord Rolle's kilns at Torrington. One of the most impressive parts of the canal is the aqueduct which carried it over the Torridge at Beam. This now forms part of the driveway to Beam House. A branch of the Grand Western Canal was constructed to Tiverton in 1814. The last canal building in the county was the Hackney canal, opened in 1843. Because of the undulating terrain some means of changing levels was necessary, usually achieved in Devon by the employment of inclined planes rather than locks.

In the second half of the eighteenth century there were a number of schemes to link the English Channel and the Bristol Channel by a canal through the south-western peninsula. In 1792 a plan for a Grand Western Canal was put forward to consist of a canal from Topsham to Taunton, with a branch to Tiverton, to connect with a canal from Taunton to Bristol. Work was begun, in 1812, on the middle section between Holcombe and Tiverton and this was completed in 1814, but unfortunately costs far exceeded the estimate and the company never had the money to construct the rest of the canal. With no major terminals, the completed section was never prosperous but it was used for the carriage of stone and coal until 1924. It then fell into disrepair but has recently been restored as an amenity waterway. This photograph shows the restored canal near Halberton

The Exeter & Crediton Navigation was surveyed by Robert Cartwright in 1800 and authorised in 1801 with a capital of £21,400. Among the subscribers to it was Exeter Corporation. Construction began between Exeter and Exwick in 1810 and in a year about half a mile was excavated but the work then ceased and the project was abandoned in 1818. This seal was attached to the official documents of the canal company

Exeter canal dates back to 1564-6 when John Trewe of Glamorgan cut a $1\frac{3}{4}$-mile channel to by-pass the weirs in the Exe at Countess Wear. On this canal he made the first use of pound locks in Britain. The canal was extended almost to Topsham in 1675-7 and again improved in 1699-1701. But the present canal is really the work of James Green who dredged and straightened it in 1820-1 and, between 1825 and 1832, extended it to Turf, making it a total length of $5\frac{1}{2}$ miles, deepened it and built a new basin at the Exeter end. The beginning of the canal at Turf, about a mile below Topsham, can be seen here

The Bude tub-boat canal (above) was built between 1819 and 1825 to carry sea-sand from Bude to wharves near Holsworthy and Launceston for use as fertiliser on the land. The canal closed in 1891. One of the boats used on it (below) has recently been recovered from its waters. It is 15ft long and 5ft wide and is fitted with cast iron wheels so that it could be hauled up the inclined plane by horses

The Stover Canal was constructed by James Templer of Stover House between 1790 and 1795. It was nearly 2 miles long and was used to carry clay, Bovey lignite and stone to the Teign at Newton Abbot. It became disused about 1938 and closed in 1943. Taken in the 1930s, this photograph shows a string of clay barges on the canal, each carrying 36-40 tons of clay

Railways

The coming of the railway transformed the economy of Devon; it rendered other forms of transport less profitable and led to the closure of most of the canals; it facilitated the movement of people and speeded up the rural exodus; it provided a stimulus to commercial agriculture and it led to the growth of the holiday trade. Brunel's broad-gauge line from London via Bristol reached Exeter in 1844 and Plymouth in 1849 and was carried into Cornwall by the Royal Albert Bridge across the Tamar at Saltash in 1859. On the section between Exeter and Newton Abbot, Brunel experimented with atmospheric traction. Lines were then built to north Devon and the London & South Western provided an alternative route from London to Exeter in 1860.

Earlier, tramways had been built to solve particular industrial transport problems. Of most interest is the Haytor Granite tramway. In the west of Dartmoor another horsedrawn railway was built in 1823 for Sir Thomas Tyrwhitt to carry supplies the 24 miles between Plymouth and Princetown. In 1879 the Rattlebrook Peat Railway was built to bring peat down to Bridestowe and remains of other tramways are to be found elsewhere on Dartmoor.

This drawing shows the original Ivybridge viaduct built by Brunel of timber on stone piers; in 1893 it was rebuilt in stone. It carries the South Devon (now the Western Region) mainline from Exeter to Plymouth across the Erme valley

One of Brunel's less successful innovations was his adoption of the atmospheric method of propulsion for the line running westwards from Exeter. The atmospheric railway, driven by a piston attached to the train which moved along a tube between the rails by atmospheric pressure as the air in front of it was pumped out to create a vacuum, closed in 1848 only a few months after it had started operation; what remains of the Totnes pumping house (above) is now part of the premises of the Unigate dairies. More complete houses remain at Starcross and at Torre, never used by the railway but now occupied by a cash and carry company.

This 4-2-4 well-tank engine was designed by James Pearson and built by Rothwell & Company in 1853 for the Bristol & Exeter Railway. The 7ft gauge engine was given the number 2002 when the Bristol & Exeter Railway was taken over by the Great Western Railway in 1876

To link Devon and Cornwall by railway it was necessary to bridge the Tamar which is about 1,100ft wide at its narrowest point and 70ft deep with a strong tidal current. Brunel solved this problem with a bridge of two spans of 455ft combining a suspension bridge with one of a conventional type. Work began in 1849 and the upper picture shows it in progress; it took six years to build and, due to four idle years caused by financial troubles, the completed bridge was not opened until 1859. The photograph below shows both the old Brunel railway bridge and the new road bridge completed in 1961

The last line to be constructed in Devon, the standard-gauge 7-mile Bideford, Westward Ho! & Appledore Railway, was built between 1901 and 1908 and, never a commercial success, was closed by the first world war in 1917. This photograph shows a train and a third class carriage c 1901

The Haytor Granite tramway was built by George Templer and opened in September 1820 to carry granite from the Haytor quarries (see page 41) to Venntiford Quay on the Stover Canal (see page 85). It was made of granite blocks with flanges on the inside on which ran iron waggons with flangeless wheels in trains of twelve drawn by 18 horses in single file, in front for the upward journey and at the rear for the downward. This photograph shows the points on the tramway

The Torrington & Marland Railway was extended from Torrington to Peters Marland in 1880 to provide transport for the ball clay extracted by the North Devon Clay Company. From Bideford the clay was either taken to Fremington for export or to the Potteries for use in this country. This 3ft gauge section of the line was in use until 1970 but the clay is now transported by road

The London & South Western Railway extended its line from Exeter to Bideford in 1855. A further extension from Bideford to Torrington was opened on 18 July 1872. This old photograph shows Torrington station being built in 1871

St Thomas station, Exeter, was built in 1846 and was the headquarters of the old South Devon Railway, which amalgamated with the Great Western in 1878. It was for a time the main Exeter station. Its platforms were originally completely roofed in but they were subsequently lengthened and since the lower photograph was taken the roof has been completely demolished. The upper picture shows the front of the station at the beginning of the century when it was still an important station

The Lynton cliff railway, built to a Swiss design by a local family called Jones, was opened in 1890. Still working, it is powered by water from the West Lyn. It links Lynton with Lynmouth

The other cliff railway still in operation in Devon is the one in south Devon at Babbacombe near Torquay which was built in 1926.

Engineering

Tools and agricultural machinery used to be made in many places in Devon but the day of the local foundry is over. An old-established Exeter foundry, Bodley & Company, closed within the past few years while the Finch foundry at Sticklepath has recently been restored as a museum of rural craft. Even those firms which continue find they have to alter their policies in the interests of efficiency. For example, Dunsford edge tool factory used to make 6 different patterns of bill hook in $\frac{1}{2}$ inch sizes from 16 inches to 12 inches with three different styles of handle. Today they find it impossible to do this and have to restrict the number of patterns they make: the small ones are now made in the Devon patterns and the large ones in the Dorset patterns. But Devon engineering has served more than local needs: a famous name in engineering throughout the world is that of the Dartmouth engineer, Thomas Newcomen, who invented the atmospheric engine to solve the problems of pumping water from the Devon metal mines. As it turned out, it was little used in Devon due to the shortage of coal but it played a vital part in the development of industry elsewhere.

In the nineteenth century and earlier every village had its blacksmith and every town a foundry shoeing the local horses and making agricultural and domestic implements for the neighbourhood. Today these have largely closed down but a good example of one of these establishments was Panaligon's Forge in Old Town Street, Dawlish, photographed in 1938

The Finch Brothers' foundry at Sticklepath, more accurately an edge-tool factory, began work in 1814 in what was originally a cloth mill and continued until 1960 when a wall collapsed. The firm became famous in the west country for its wide range of agricultural tools and shovels for the clay industry and since it stopped work the premises have been restored and turned into a museum. The machinery, including the helve hammers above, was driven by water power from the River Taw. These 'trip' or 'tilt' hammers, believed to be unique in the west of England, were operated by a cogged wheel which lifted up the end of the shaft and then let it drop, bringing the hammer down on the metal to be beaten. Some work also had to be done by hand and the photograph below shows various hand anvils and also conveys an impression of the muddle typical of such a small workshop

In the towns foundries became larger and one of the best-known in Devon was Bodleys at Exeter which was founded in 1790 and specialised in making cast-iron gearing. This building was used to store their patterns dating from the mid-nineteenth century

The last 15ft diameter gearwheel being cast before Bodleys closed down in 1967

A foundry in Exeter which is still working is Willey & Co. This originated as a firm of gas engineers and the building shown here was their gas meter factory built in 1904. At that time the firm was the biggest in Exeter with over 1000 employees. It is now part of the United Gas Industries Group and has diversified into general engineering

This Newcomen atmospheric engine was originally put to work with another at the Griff Colliery at Nuneaton in Warwickshire and then in Oakthorpe Pit nearby. In 1821 it was sold to the Coventry Canal Company and intermittently used to pump water at Hawkesbury until 1913. Since 1963 it has been preserved at Dartmouth as a memorial to Newcomen

Morris' edge-tool factory at Dunsford is still operating. The machinery used to be driven by water power but in 1937 it turned over to electricity and an electrically-driven hammer can be seen above, shaping the shaft of a hoe or similar tool. The factory employs 40 people, mainly men, at present

This splendid Norwich Union firemark, still painted in its original colours, can be seen tucked under the thatched eaves of the Dunsford factory. In the days when the insurance companies maintained their own fire brigades the buildings insured by them had to carry their firemark so that it was obvious which company was responsible and who should put out the fire

Stephens, Brain & Company's foundry in High Street, Bideford, ran a shop selling its own products and associated wares and also undertook plumbing, electrical and gas fitting while decorating its shopfront with a fine example of its workmanship

Miscellaneous Industries

Besides the large and well-known industries of Devon—cloth, paper and mining—there are here, as elsewhere, many smaller industries largely catering for local needs and using local raw materials. In Devon, many of these were associated with the processing of agricultural produce while another important group was concerned with the provision of public utilities—the supply of gas, water and electricity. A recent development has been the revival on a new basis of an old local industry serving more than local needs, glass making.

While the history of 'The Old Match Factory' in Exeter is obscure, it is clear that matches were never made there. A woollen mill occupied the site in 1563 but this building claims to date from 1774. In the 1850s it was a flax mill and behind it was a rectangular 'retting pond' in which the flax was soaked so that the live tissue rotted and only fibre was left. Since about 1860 it has belonged to Trews Weir paper mill who have produced hand-made paper bags there and used it as a stable and a warehouse

With the coming of the railways enabling rapid distribution throughout the country dairying became a major industry in Devon and is today carried on on a large scale. One of the oldest creameries in the county is the one at Hemyock. As in other industries, processes have been modernised, as this churn-tipper shows

Glass for local use was made in Devon as early as the seventeenth century but then the industry died out. The manufacture of glass for a quality market has recently been re-introduced into the county at Torrington by the Dartington Hall Trustees, who are using Swedish workmen to train local men in their modern factory shown above

Water supply is an often neglected industry but, in Devon at least, it has a long history. Devonport leat was constructed to supply water from the West Dart, the Cowsic and the Blackbrook to Devonport. It included in its course a number of aqueducts and a 648-yard tunnel near Nun's Cross. This drawing by John Swete was made soon after its inauguration in 1793

In many towns in the county, water conduits survive in the streets. At Beer and at Hemyock they have been converted into lamp standards. This conduit at Dartmouth was originally constructed in 1599 and rebuilt in 1847

By the early twentieth century natural sources of water were inadequate to meet growing demands and reservoirs had to be built to store water. This photograph by Robert Burnard shows the construction of the dam on Vennford Brook at Swincombe for Paignton Water Works in August 1904

Exeter acquired a gasworks in 1817 and was one of the first provincial cities to do so. From there gas making spread to other parts of the county but today, with rationalisation, there are no gasworks still operating in the county and the remaining gas-holders are used for storage. Below is a drawing of the original gas-holder house in Tudor Street, Exeter and a plan of the retorts. Left is an old gas purifier at Chagford. In this process the gas was passed over oxide of iron to remove the sulphur

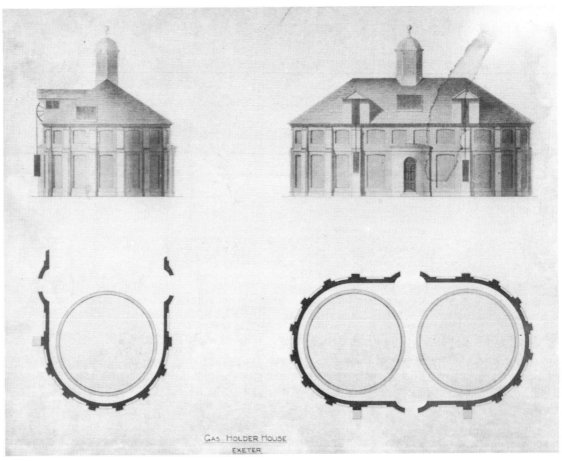

GAS HOLDER HOUSE
EXETER

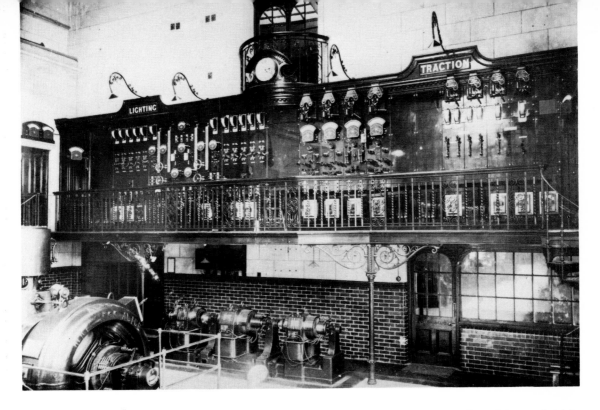

Electric lighting was introduced into Britain in 1875; eight years later a demonstration of it was held in Exeter and in 1889 an Electric Light Company was formed. Plymouth was slower to adopt the new source of power and its streets were not lit by electricity until 1899. Taken soon after this service began, the upper photograph shows the switchboard of the Devonport substation in Plymouth and below is an exterior view of the same substation which supplied power for the trams from Stonehouse to Devonport as well as for lighting needs

One of the only two factories in the country which still tans leather by the oak-bark method and the only factory which tans and curries leather is in Devon at Colyton. It produces surgical and saddle leather which requires leather of a particular quality. To get the leather to the required thickness it has to be shaved on the rough side and this is done on machines like the one shown here

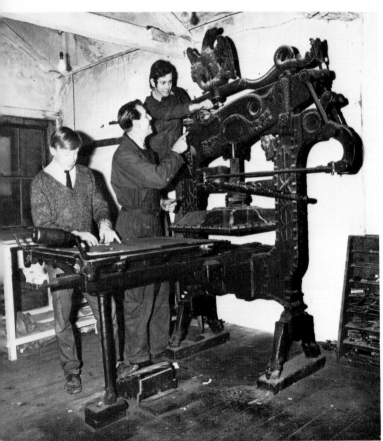

A much more widespread industry was printing. Little now survives of the machinery earlier used in printing works in the county but this Eagle Columbia Press, dating from 1830 and used by the *Exmouth Herald* until 1970, is now in Sidmouth museum

Housing

Early industrial housing on the domestic basis in which houses of clothworkers and others also contained the workshops has largely disappeared in Devon, but as industry moved away from the existing settlements other forms of industrial housing became necessary. To attract labour to the isolated mines of Dartmoor and to swell the population of expanding towns such as Tiverton, landlords and industrialists built houses to accommodate their workers and examples of these are still to be found. Most of it took the form of housing such as can be seen at Hennock, Morwellham, Tiverton and elsewhere, but in some cases hostels were considered more appropriate. At Haytor Vale one was built to house the men working in the quarries.

Some of the few remaining woolworkers' cottages are at Buckfastleigh. The wooden slatted top storey, which can also be seen on mills such as Belford Mill in Ashburton, was used as a wool store and for stretching the warp threads

The housing of industrial workers on new sites away from towns always posed a problem which was often solved by the construction of industrial villages. In the early twentieth century Teign Village, Hennock, was built to house men employed at the Great Rock and Shuttamore mines

The City of Exeter Improved Industrial Buildings Company was founded in 1873 with the object of 'providing commodious and healthy dwellings for the poorer classes'. The first tenement-block to be completed was Follett Buildings in Mermaid Yard, a site off South Street previously occupied by a brewery, which was named after C. J. Follett, the mayor and chairman of the company, and opened in 1874. Then followed Hampton and Kendall Buildings in Blackboy Road in 1876 and lastly Cotton Buildings, again in Mermaid Yard, in 1877. Cotton Buildings has recently been demolished but the others remain. Follett (illustrated here) and Cotton Buildings are of four storeys while Hampton and Kendall Buildings are brick three-storied buildings, parallel to one another with a long narrow courtyard between and a central passage

At Haytor Vale cottages as well as a hostel were built in the 1820s to house the men working in the quarries

When John Heathcoat started his lace factory at Tiverton in 1816 he built several terraces of houses for the workers, many of whom came from Loughborough with Heathcoat

Acknowledgements

The production of this book would not have been possible without the help of many people who have provided photographs and ideas. I am particularly grateful to Celia King; Frank Booker, Kate Havinden, W. G. Hoskin the University of Exeter photographer, Barry Hughes and John Perkins have also helped in various ways.

I should like to thank the following individuals and firms for the pictures indicated: W. R. J. Baker, 75a; James Barber, 107; W. P. Beach, 70a, 71a; Martin Blythe, 82; J. C. Brierley, 83b; Bernard Chapman, 23a, 93; J. Somers Cocks, 86; A. W. Everitt, 103a; J. C. Ferguson, 45, 46; Tony Freeman, 38a, 50a; Basil Greenhill, 70b; Charles Hadfield, 83a; Kate Havinden, 22a, 38b, 109a; W. G. Hoskin, 10, 14b, 27, 30, 70a, 71a, 77c, 79a, 91b; Barry Hughes, 24b, 25b, 39b, 65a, 80b, 90a, 90b, 99; D. H. Jones, 94b; Dennis Kemp, 13a, 31a, 77a, 81a, 98a, 98b; R. W. Kidner, 53b; C. M. King, 39a, 63a, 76b, 108b; Cyril McCombe, 94a, 95a; Ron Pearce, 84b; John Perkins, 73; E. N. Masson Phillips, 77b; R. F. Rew, 104a; P. H. G. Richardson, 44a, 44b; John Rottenbury, 47b; Lady Sayer, 103b; A. J. Scrivens, 95b; Sir Kelvin Spencer, 24a; Alan Stoyel, 11a; A. R. Tucker, 31b; J. Tucker, 78; Rex Wailes, 28a; Mark Westaway, 84a; Axminster Carpets Ltd, 16b; J. & F. J. Baker & Co Ltd, 106a; British Rail, 87a, 91a; Cement and Concrete Association, 74; Coates & Co (Plymouth) Ltd, 32a, 32b; Dartington Glass Ltd, 102a; John Heathcoat & Co Ltd, 109b; Hutchings of Appledore, 70b; *Illustrated London News*, 33a; Walter Jenkins & Co Ltd, 40b; Unigate Creameries Ltd, 101; John Vicary & Sons Ltd, 11b, 13b; Watts, Blake, Bearne & Co Ltd, 52a, 63b, 85; West of England Newspapers, 34, 35a, 40a, 52b; *Western Morning News*, 14a, 15b, 25a, 53a, 56a, 88b; *Western Times*, 17, 43a, 43b, 79b, 100; Wiggins Teape Paper Mills Ltd, 18a, 18b, 19a, 19b, 20b; Willeys of Exeter, 96.

I am also grateful to the following museums and their staffs for help in finding illustrations: Bideford Library and Museum, 12b, 49a, 59, 66, 72a, 72b, 89a; Brixham Museum, 68a; Dartmouth Museum, 31b, 69; Devon County Library, 67b, 81b; Devon Record Office, from the Chapman Collection (D 1578), 20a, 23b, 42, 58b, 92a, 108a, and from J. B. Swete's 'Picturesque sketches of Devon' (D 564), 102b; Exeter City Library, 21, 61, 62a, 104b; Ilfracombe Library, 60; National Maritime Museum, 67a, 71b; Plymouth Public Libraries, 36, 45, 46, 80a, 87b, 88a, 105a, 105b; Royal Albert Memorial Museum, Exeter, 14b; Sidmouth Museum, 106b; Torbay Public Library, 92b; Torquay Natural History Society, 47a, 50b, 57a, 57b, 58a.

The Geological Survey provided 37b, 48a, 48b, 49b, 51, 54, 55, and the National Monuments Record, to whose staff I am grateful, made available 12a, 16a, 62b, 64a, 64b, 65b, 75b. These photographs are Crown Copyright.

Illustrations were also taken from the following books: Alfred Barnard, *Noted Breweries of Great Britain and Ireland* (London, 1889-91), 28b, 29a, 29b, 35b; British Medical Association, *A Book of the South West* (Exeter: Pollard, 1907), 37a, 68b; *Devon and Cornwall Notes and Queries*, XI (1920-21), 22b; Benjamin Donn, *A map of the county of Devon 1765*, ed William L. D. Ravenhill (Exeter: Devon and Cornwall Record Society and University of Exeter, 1965), 9; Michael C. Ewans, *The Haytor Granite Tramway and Stover Canal* (Newton Abbot: David & Charles, 1966), 41, 89b; Walter E. Minchinton, *Industrial Archaeology of Devon* (Dartington Amenity Research Trust, 1973), 15a, 26; Alfred Pollard and Frederick W. Beech, *Cider-making* (Hart-Davis, 1957), 36; Mark Searle, *Turnpikes and Toll-bars* (Hutchinson, 1930), 76a; C. Malcolm Watkins, *North Devon Pottery and Its Export to America in the 17th Century* (Washington, DC: Smithsonian Institution, 1960), 56b; George Watkins, *The Stationary Steam Engine* (Newton Abbot: David & Charles, 1968), 97.

Relevant Books

Frank Booker, *Industrial Archaeology of the Tamar Valley*. David & Charles, 1967

Michael Bouquet, *Westcountry Sail: Merchant Shipping 1840–1960*. David & Charles, 1971

Vernon Boyle and Donald Payne, *Devon Harbours*. Christopher Johnson, 1952

Gordon A. Brown, John D. C. A. Prideaux and Harold G. Radcliff, *The Lynton & Barnstaple Railway*. David & Charles, 1964

Michael Chitty, *A Guide to Industrial Archaeology in Exeter*. Exeter Industrial Archaeology Group, 1971

Joseph H. Collins, *Observations on the West of England Mining Region: Being an Account of the Mineral Deposits and Economic Geology of the Region*. Plymouth, 1912

William Crossing, *Dartmoor Worker*, ed Brian Le Messurier. David & Charles, 1966

——, *A Hundred Years on Dartmoor*, ed Brian Le Messurier. David & Charles, 1967

Michael C. Ewans, *The Haytor Granite Tramway and Stover Canal*. David & Charles, 2nd ed, 1966

Crispin Gill, ed, *Dartmoor: A New Study*. David & Charles, 1970

Basil Greenhill and Ann Giffard, *Westcountrymen in Prince Edward's Isle*. Toronto UP and David & Charles, 1967

Charles Hadfield, *Atmospheric Railways: A Victorian Venture in Silent Speed*. David & Charles, 1967

——, *The Canals of South-west England*. David & Charles, 1967

Helen Harris, *Industrial Archaeology of Dartmoor*. David & Charles, 1968

——, and Monica Ellis, *The Bude Canal*. David & Charles, 1972

Williams G. Hoskins, *Devon*. Collins, 1954; David & Charles, 1972

——, *Old Devon*. David & Charles, 1966; Pan, 1971

Kenneth Hudson, *The History of English China Clays*. David & Charles, 1969

J. Kenneth Major, *Finch Brothers' Foundry*. David & Charles, 1966

Walter E. Minchinton, *Industrial Archaeology in Devon*. Devon County Council, 2nd ed, 1973

——, and John Perkins, *Tidemills of Devon and Cornwall*. Exeter Industrial Archaeology Group, 1972
Archaeology Group, 1972

Michael Oppenheim, *The Maritime History of Devon*, ed Walter E. Minchinton. University of Exeter, 1968

Alfred Shorter, *Papermaking in the British Isles*. David & Charles, 1971

Hugh W. Strong, *Industries of North Devon*. Barnstaple, 1889; David & Charles, 1971

John M. Slader, *Days of Renown: the Story of Mining on Exmoor and the Border Parishes*. West Country Handbooks, 1965

Douglas Stuckey, *The Bideford, Westward Ho! and Appledore Railway, 1901–1917*. West Country Handbooks, 1962

——, *Adventurers' Slopes: the Story of the Silver and Other Mines of Combe Martin in Devon*. West Country Handbooks, 1965

David St John Thomas, *A Regional History of the Railways of Great Britain, 1. The West Country*. David & Charles, 4th ed, 1973

William White, *History, Gazetteer and Directory of the County of Devon*. Sheffield: W. White, 1850, 1878, 1890; 1850 edition reprinted with an introduction by Walter E. Minchinton, David & Charles, 1968

Richard G. Hansford Worth, *Dartmoor*, ed Guy M. Spooner and Frederick S. Russell. David & Charles, 1967

Joyce Youings, *Tuckers Hall Exeter*. University of Exeter, 1968